LOVESICK:

POEMS & STORIES TO TURN YOU ON

LOVESICK:

POEMS & STORIES TO TURN YOU ON

By Kareema Edwards

Chubby Girl From Brooklyn Publishing

LOVESICK
Poems & Stories to Turn You On

ISBN: 978-0-578-77736-8

Published by Chubby Girl From Brooklyn Publishing
New York, New York
Printed in the United States of America
First Edition 2020

Editing: Smart Girl Media // TaiiaSmartYoung.com

This one is for my husband, Teddy,
my son Kareem, my daughter Seona
and my angels, my Mommy and Daddy
(Ophelia McClain and Joseph Johnson Sr.)

CONTENTS

"A woman isn't a whore for wanting pleasure.
If it were unnatural we would not be born with such desires."

–Nenia Campbell

FOREPLAY

There are guilty pleasures like binge watching your favorite Netflix show, eating cookies and cream ice cream straight out of the carton and scrolling on Instagram to see what your high school ex is up to this week. And then there is *Lovesick*, a super sexy and super steamy look into naughty escapades and deep desires you think about when the lights are low and Maxwell is inviting you to slip those panties off to do a little sumthin' sumthin'.

But here's the question: Are you brave enough to tell your lover about your fantasy? *Lovesick* is a series of poems and vignettes ("Poison," "Who Is She to You?" and "Trade It All") that draw you in and get you hooked. Remember when you were obsessed with Zane's *Addicted* or *Gettin' Buck Wild*? Well, prepare to be lovesick. Don't forget to check out the super sexy "You Got Me," which is a bonus read. You might see these characters pop up in Kareema's next book.

Lovesick is only for the sexy people. Read at your own risk.

—Denice Rivera

INTRO

THE PLEASURE PRINCIPLE

THE PLEASURE PRINCIPLE

Let's be honest. We don't really like to talk about threesomes for fear of being judged. There. I said it. Threesomes are those taboo trysts that are more situationship than relationship because the only thing you and your partner are committed to is satisfaction. With threesomes, couples either desire a little something extra to spice up a boring sex life or they're craving additional heat to an already spicy situation. My suggestion is live life. Just know that there are some risks involved.

Lust and desire have the ability to cloud your judgement. Don't let multiple orgasms overrule common sense. I believe that if you do something constantly, like eat a chocolate candy bar twice a week, and it tastes delicious and feels amazing, it has the ability to become an addiction. Threesomes, so I've heard, will get you open and there will always be one person that feels stronger about the sexual bond than the other. The result can lead to someone becoming lovesick. When you're lovesick, you are totally off balance. You might want someone who doesn't belong to you, even if those feelings aren't reciprocated.

I've had this conversation with my girlfriends over cocktails and the reactions ranged from curious to outraged. To be fair, I've also talked to men about this subject and let's just say their opinion is quite different from the ladies. Guys love the idea of sexual freedom, so a threesome or even an open relationship (which has its own set of rules and understandings) is ideal for them. Some were enthralled by the idea of having a threesome or being able to sexually express themselves outside of their relationship *without* losing their partner. But they didn't want to level the playing field. It wasn't cool for their girlfriends and wives to have her own trysts or invite another man into their bedroom. Some guys were horrified and became territorial with the thought of another man touching their lady. Others were cool with their women getting a little side action as long as the person knew about the main relationship.

Me? What do I think? I'm a sexually forward thinker and these conversations about sex and threesomes and open relationships are fascinating. Again, live life. As a poet, I write and perform material about relationships and sexually taboo topics. This collection features poems and short stories from my wild imagination about how some people navigate and give in to their sexual desires.

PART 1

KINDLING

WHO IS SHE TO YOU?

It was never my intention to let things go as far as they did. In the end, I got a lot more than I bargained for during my sexual self-discovery phase. Daymien and I were in an open relationship and I can't lie, there were moments when having threesomes were deeply exhilarating. But there were also moments when I questioned myself. I wanted to be enough. I wanted to be the only woman he desired, but since variety is the spice of life, I went with the flow. My girls were like, "that could never be me" and I'm sure his guys were like, "that lucky bastard!" Both sides were probably right.

The rules of engagement allowed me to have my own trysts, which led me to understand the rush of excitement that Day experienced. But I had boundaries with—let's call them The Other Party. I was always honest about my relationship, respectful and direct, and all of my episodes never lasted too long. Foolishly, I thought this would prevent me or The Other Party from forming an attachment. Having another person crave me and shower me with gifts was to quote Sade, "the sweetest taboo." Soon, things became overwhelming because The Other Party required more than I was willing to give.

Honestly, I enjoyed escapades with Day and other women the most. At first, it was a lot to process seeing my honey be sexual with another woman. The first time, I was a bit uncomfortable, but totally engrossed in the scene. Captivated is the best word I can use to describe my reaction to her response to his touch. I wondered if she felt the same way I did. He wore lust on his face with her and it was so sexy. That's when I discovered that I was a voyeur on the low.

The Internet will forever be undefeated. I often socialized on the Curvaceous Cuties website. I loved all of my interactions because the women were cool and friendly, and the men were handsome and funny. I met Miley on this site. Miley was beautiful with caramel skin, hazel eyes, sandy brown hair and dangerous curves. Her happy disposition matched her dope conversation. Once, during one of our great talks she dropped a bomb that shocked and intrigued me.

"Jazz, tell me something, have you ever found yourself attracted to women?" Miley asked.

I took a moment to compose my thoughts. "Yes, I have. Women are beautiful." I could tell by her banter that she was pleased with my answer. She sent me a private message and revealed that she was attracted to me and wanted to hangout. That was cool with me, plus it was possible since she only lived two hours away in Connecticut. We made plans for her to spend the weekend at my home. This is how my journey into threesomes began.

I was so excited that I didn't check in with Day about this rendezvous. This was going to be an interesting conversation. I wondered how he'd feel about Miley spending the weekend with us, but more importantly, how he'd feel about her wanting me. I logged off the computer to text him. When he got home, I explained that my new friend Miley was coming to spend the weekend with us. I wish I could've captured the look on his face.

"So how do you feel about that?" I asked.

His answer, "It's all good."

Later that night in bed, Day rolled over and said, "Are you gonna let her lick that pussy, while you suck on this hard dick?"

"Don't say that," I whimpered. I was so turned on. I was damn near dripping.

"Why can't I say that?" He climbed on top of me and pinned my hands over my head. "Tell me. Why can't I ask? Is it because you're getting wet right now?"

What I said next sent him over the edge. "Yes, it is."

He kissed me, then spread my legs wide open and dove in tongue first. I whined on his face like my favorite dancehall song just came on the radio. He came up for air and slid inside of me. My juices covered his face in a shiny grin. With each thrust he elevated me to heights of ecstasy. I knew the thought of another woman touching me aroused him, and I fantasized about how he'd react once Miley came to visit us the following weekend.

"How do you want it?" he asked, pulling himself out of me to rub his head on my clit.

"Harder," I whispered.

"I can't hear you. How do you want it?" he breathed in my ear.

"Harder!" I yelled, playing along with our usual game. "Harder!"

With each stroke he pumped a little bit harder until he collapsed.

Before she arrived, I took a luxurious green tea bubble bath, I moisturized my skin with shea and cocoa butter, and put on my favorite perfume. Even though we'd be relaxing at home, I wanted to look good. I wore a nude-colored dress with black lace boy shorts underneath. I never feel complete without sexy panties. I enjoyed a glass of wine as I watched my honey. A rush of heat swirled around in my body. Day looked so damn good with a fresh haircut, tapered beard, black fitted T-shirt and sweats. To top it off, he smelled as good as he looked. Kenneth Cole Black cologne hung in the air. Tonight was going to be something special.

The doorbell rang and we stared at each other for a few seconds before he casually walked to the door. When I heard her voice, it hit me—she's here and this is really happening. We welcomed Miley to our home with hugs and open arms and she was all smiles. Her pictures didn't do her justice. As Day put her bags away, I told her to make herself comfortable. I offered her something to drink and sat down beside her. Our conversation was easy, but the tension was noticeable, so she broke the ice. "Jazz, I'll be honest. I'm so excited to be here with you. I kept looking at the calendar thinking, 'Friday, hurry up!' Now I'm here and I plan on taking advantage of every moment."

Miley leaned in close. My heart raced. I felt chills. Was she about to kiss me? Oh, my yes, she was. Our lips met and an aching sound escaped from somewhere deep inside me. I didn't recognize my own voice. That must have been confirmation that it was okay to go in for the kill. Her lips were so soft and she smelled sweet. Her scent was intoxicating, more so than the wine. Our tongues danced in each other's mouths and her hands rubbed my thighs. When I opened my eyes to see the look of sheer pleasure on her face it turned me on even more. Breathless, I pulled away to control myself. I'd kissed a woman before, but not like this. My panties were soaked and my nipples were erect. I cleared my throat and excused myself to process what was about to happen.

"Take all the time you need, beautiful," Miley said as I left the room.

I took a shower to calm the storm brewing between my legs, and my body was sensitive to the touch. Gently, I stroked my nipples and each time felt better than the last. I spread my legs and got into the perfect position to "pop off." Using my index finger, I rubbed my clit in a circular motion, making it wet and sticky. My legs shook. I rubbed faster and I just as I got close to my breaking point, I stopped. I love the buildup. Then, I put one finger on my clit and one inside. Leaning against the shower wall, I stood there grinding on my finger. My clit swelled. I didn't know that I could make myself feel this good.

When I turned off the shower, I heard sounds coming from the living room. Wrapped in a towel, I crept out of the bathroom to see the mood had been set with soft jazz and candles. They started without me.

Day stood up as Miley kneeled to give him head. She took a break from deep throating to tell him, "You taste so fuckin' good. I'm not going to miss an inch."

I was so engrossed in their activity that I hadn't noticed that Day had been watching me. "Baby, come here and drop that towel. I couldn't help myself. Her mouth wanted this dick. Shit feels so good. You should get down here and show Miley what I like," he said. His eyes were locked on me as he spoke.

"It looks like she knows exactly what you like," I said, searching for the best seat to watch the action. "I'm enjoying the show."

"I told you to do something and now you want to show off. You know what that means? Spanking time," he said. He ordered me to get on the couch and bend over. As soon as I arched my back, the spanking began. I had a feeling Day was going to be a beast tonight.

Miley watched for a little bit and then she walked around to the other side of the couch to kiss me. Her mouth tasted like Day. Behind me I heard a growl and then I felt another hard smack on my ass. My sounds were silenced by Miley's kisses. A series of smacks followed.

Suddenly, he grabbed my hair, made me lie on my back and as soon as my head hit the couch, Miley buried her face between my legs. The licks were slow and deliberate, then she started licking ferociously, while squeezing my nipples. She took her tongue and stuck it in and out at lightning speed. My body shook and craved more. Day watched us and stroked his rock hard dick.

He stared at me with so much lust in his eyes, it was unnerving. Then, he walked over to the table to get a condom. My heart almost beat out of my chest. I knew what was about to happen. He opened the condom and walked behind Miley. He was about to fuck another woman. Before I could finish my thought, he entered her from behind. From my position on the couch, I stared—horny and confused—as my honey pumped, grunted and threw his head back.

Miley fingered me while slowly sucking my clit. "That's right, ride my face, while daddy fucks me. Fuck me, daddy," Miley begged. "Don't stop. Yes, long strokes, uhhhhh, I'm about to cum."

When Miley reached her climax, she screamed and Day nearly lost it, sending him into overdrive. "Fuck, this pussy is good baby," he said panting. "Thank you for doing this." He pulled off the condom and came on Miley's back as she continued to feast on me. This intensified my orgasm. Exhausted, Miley and Day fell on the couch. We breathed heavily and in sync with each other. The silence forced me to think, but I didn't want to because my emotions ranged from euphoria to confusion. I couldn't believe what we just did.

WAVE

With each stroke

My tears threaten to choke

Steal my breath

have me in distress

Lust doesn't evoke this type of passion

Chills running up and down

my spine is a natural reaction

in this moment I refuse to be passive

as he goes deeper

I match his thrust

I won't give up

I'm his possession

The towel I won't throw in

Wave hit, "Oh, Gawd"

Euphoria

This is becoming tribal

We're going at it like warriors

Heat, screaming, gasping, heavy breathing

Moaning in my ear

"I love you. I'm never leaving"

Tears, embraces, kisses to my face

Eye contact replaces words

Consciousness fades away

WOMAN

Looks exchanged
Accelerated heart rate
Breathing labored
Touches savored
These moments
I want to last forever
as time goes by, we try
to make great better
Your hugs are the best
I hide my tears in your chest
Synchronized heartbeats
tells the story of you and me
Perfectly flawed
highs and lows
We're still standing
No matter what blows
No matter what life throws
Emotions so raw
when I think of us
I'm totally in awe
But in moments like this
when everything is quiet and still
Standing heart to heart
I know this is how
I always want to feel
Nothing stolen
I've earned each moment
And I enjoy the beauty of being a woman

LIKE WE USED TO DO

You don't touch me like you used to

kiss me like you used to

Maybe there's someone else

She can give tips that are useful

Tonight, I'mma step it up a bit

Walk in the house and handle my biz

No phone

No TV

No kids

When you see me

I want to be taken down savagely

Baby, I need you to ravish me

Body will be glistening to perfection

That if you look closely

you'll see your reflection

Tonight, there will be no wasted erection

just love making so euphoric

You'll feel a heavenly presence

Tonight, you're gonna kiss me like you used to

touch me like you used to

do all the things that we used to

SESSIONS NO. 2: HIS EYES

Eyes met from
across the room
attraction was immediate
He looked like a meal
he had all the right ingredients
His eyes said it all,
His stature was tall
His complexion, mahogany
His head was bald
His scent was musk
mint and patchouli
From the both of us
attraction was oozing
I was practically drooling
His smile was perfect
I was enamored
Damn near swooning
On my lips
there was a song
And I began crooning,
"Baby, you are
everything and
everything is you"
He smiled and said,
"I knew you
were a poet

I didn't know

you could sing

you seem to

have talent flowing

through your veins."

I replied with a bashful smile

"Thank you kindly, sir

I've been doing

both for a while."

His eyes said it all

His handshake was gentle

 I was totally enthralled

STRETCHING

Whew, that felt great
fresh out the shower
don't want to be late
Pat myself dry put on my favorite scent
Cucumber melon with a dash of mint
Shea butter to soften my skin
sometimes, I add cocoa butter
for that perfect blend
Spread my legs and start to bend
About to get my stretch on, so let me begin
Touch my toes and rise again
until I complete 4 sets of 10
lying on my back taking deep breaths
from my shoulders down I start to caress
Work my way back up
now I'm on my breast
Feels so good I must confess
Sounds escape as I gyrate my hips
Didn't know I could make
myself feel like this
Legs spread still on the floor
I'm home alone might as well explore
Part those folds that lead to my core
insert one finger, yeah need one more
Rub that bud that's the center of me
feel so good to just center on me

I'm so hot, need a sprinkler on me

Self-love is the best love

That shit feels great

I'm almost there the dam

is about to break

Ahhh, yes that's just what I need

My afternoon stretches

have just been completed

TEMPTATION

It could've
popped off
but I only asked
to be dropped off
Looked me up down
and said, "Damn your
ass looks mad soft."
All I could do
was silently pray
that he's looking at
the road, but
his hand is
on my leg
My heart is
starting to race
He makes a
right turn, but my
house is not
this way
I'm silent at
this point just sitting
back relaxing
He parked in
front of his
house and it
wasn't by accident

READ BETWEEN THE LINES

When I say no with the moan

you know I don't mean it

You can tell by my reaction

and the way that I'm breathing

When I say stop, yet I assist

when you start to go hard

I make no attempts to resist

When you pull my hair and moan

"Daddy, please..." Translation?

What's taking so long

for you to be inside me

When I say don't

I really mean I do

I love what foreplay leads up to

The intensity is what pushes me over the edge

So many times, you've fucked me hard in my head

Baby, read the signs, they say so much

If I didn't want you then

I wouldn't let you touch

The beginning of it all is essential

If you want my body, you

must get into my mental

Guys could get a lot further

if they just took their time

listen to what she wants and read between the lines

ANTICIPATION

I got my locs pulled up
my lip gloss poppin'
black lace boy shorts
Tank top cotton
I smell intoxicatin'
I look even better
just a few finishing touches
it will all come together
Anticipation has me so intrigued
we vibe so well we have perfect chemistry
I love when he touches me and pulls me near
he teases me when
I run my fingers through my hair
He makes me so nervous, but it's the best kind
I often fantasize about him being mine
Tonight is the night and he's so worthy
Candles everywhere, he certainly deserves this
Glanced at myself in the mirror yes, I look like candy
This is long overdue, can't wait for him
to manhandle me
Anticipation is a bitch
I remain patient
I want him so bad that
I can damn near taste it

FORNICATION

You are so amazing
keep me captivated
To say that I'm feeling you
is an understatement
You're constantly asking me,
"When are you gonna let me taste it?"
Time is of the essence
we really shouldn't waste it
so, I'm giving in
Damn, you've been patient
please promise you'll be gentle
when your tongue penetrates it
It's finally happening, what a joyous occasion
later that night I climaxed and screamed
like the bird that was caged in
My baby deserved a standing ovation
'Cause he took me to infinite heights of elevation
This kinda thing could be dangerous
thank God I'm never scared
Always quite courageous

THE AUDACITY

The words you uttered left me floored
Owe you? I don't even know you
Starting to question why I picked up the phone for you
There are too many things you don't do
Yeah, you got bread, dress nice and handsome too
The audacity! How dare you ask for a threesome?
Why do you feel you're worthy?
List your reasons. I just need one
You're not ready for that smoke
In a room full of yeses
There are no no's
The audacity to think you can hang
So the other person can laugh at me?
This lifestyle is complete savagery
you can't come halfway
You would be needed at full capacity
again, the audacity
I find it hilarious that you even asked me

SESSION NO. 4: PREPPING

Candles are arranged perfectly
fresh out the shower
I feel a sense of urgency
body adorned with
the perfume and oil
that he purchased for me
I'm as nervous as can be
I've been looking
forward to this
night all damn week
lingerie hugging every
curve nice and neat
black lace and satin top
barely there skirt with pleats
sexy ass heels
to dress up my feet
pink lipstick, my locs
nice and curly makes
my look complete
looking in the mirror
I'm satisfied with what I see
I can't wait for my baby
to get home to me
but until he does
let me give myself a treat
standing against the wall

Lovesick

with my legs spread apart
slowly touching myself
until my inner me
starts to throb
1 finger in
body starting to shake
2 fingers in
my body is about
to quake
I pulled them both out
umm, the aftermath
I love the taste
okay I have
to get it together
he should be here
any second
what's date night
without a little prepping

PART 2

INFERNO

POISON

One day, while perusing Let's Mingle, one of my favorite sites, I noticed a new friend request from Lucky Jewel. I didn't recognize the name, so I looked to see if we had mutual friends. One name stood out: Shawn Matters. I wondered how many degrees of separation there were between Miss Jewel and my man. My curiosity was piqued, so I added her. It didn't take long to receive a message from Lucky Jewel. It read, "I hope we can be cool."

I told her that I'm always down for new friendships. "My page is private. How did you find me?" I asked, genuinely intrigued.

"Your hubby and I grew up together. I was going through his pics and when I saw you, I was like, 'Oh, she is pretty,'" Lucky wrote back.

Well, she's mad forward, I thought. But I liked her candor.

"I told Shawn that I want to meet his sexy ass wife," she said. "But he was scared, worried that I might take you from him."

I laughed to myself before typing, "Thank you for the compliment. He never mentioned any of this to me."

That ended our exchange, but now my thoughts were all over the place and I had hella questions. Later that evening when Shawn got home, I told him that I traded messages with Lucky and that I knew about her request. Sitting on the gray couch, he let his head drop to his chest like a little boy who'd been caught sneaking cookies before dinner.

"Babe, care to explain yourself?" I said, joining him on the couch.

He scratched his head and put the remote on the table. He explained that he never expected one of his exes to be attracted to his current woman. "Judging by this conversation and that damn smirk on your face you want to meet her," he said, searching my face for more clues.

I bit the inside of my cheek to keep a straight face. I kinda liked seeing him squirm. "Are you jealous?" I said.

He shifted his weight to the edge of the couch. Maybe there was more to this story. "Bree, Lucky and I had an intense situation, but we stayed friends. I have no problem with you two being cool, but I know that she has always had a thing for girls," he said, filling in the missing pieces.

Now I understood why he might be reluctant for us to be friendly. But other thoughts crept in my head, like did he have unfinished business with Lucky? Did he still have feelings for her? As my mind raced to recall old stories, I remembered that Shawn had mentioned Lucky once or twice before, but he always downplayed their connection.

Lucky and I became Internet besties. I liked her vibe. She was a free spirit that was always in a good mood. Lucky schooled me about Flames, a new website targeted to people eager to add something extra to their relationship or open to have a no-strings attached situation. Lucky was a star on the site. And unlike other sites, Flames' chatrooms had web cameras. It didn't take long for Lucky to request to see my "beautiful face" and for me to become addicted to Flames. Everyone flocked to our chatroom and we always wore something sexy to entertain our guests. Often, we coordinated our colors to drive the men crazy. They'd send us heart emojis followed by offers to meet in private chatrooms. Shawn never said anything about my connection to Lucky or the chatrooms, but I knew all of it annoyed him. Soon, Lucky and I elevated our friendship to phone calls and text messages with pictures. It was all very innocent like, "Hey, what do you think of this outfit? Do you think my husband will like it?" Lucky was married, but outside of those texts about fashion, she rarely brought him up.

Our bond continued to grow, but something between us began to feel different. In the Flames' chatrooms she told our fans that I was her wife. That was how we got down, so I never thought anything of it. It didn't take long before things changed. During one of our usual phone chats Lucky complained about being bored at home in Poughkeepsie, with nothing to do in town besides retail or food therapy. I suggested that she and hubby go for a drive or to the movies, but he was out of town.

"He's out of town and he left without servicing me. So I am bored and horny," Lucky shared. We both laughed. After I suggested that she take matters into her own hands, she dropped a bomb that I wasn't prepared for.

"Bree, you're right. I should do that. Care to help me out?" Lucky said.

I'm not sure how long the silence lasted, but it felt like forever.

Then, I cleared my throat. "How am I supposed to do that?"

"Video chat me and I'll tell you."

I paused. What had I just gotten myself into? Is this what Shawn thought would happen? There was only one way to find out. I logged on to video chat with her. Lucky was dark skinned with beautiful eyes and juicy, soft lips. She was the poster girl for thick thighs saves lives. Lucky pushed her chair away from the computer to reveal her naked, oiled body. She spread her legs wide to reveal a mound of plump brown and pink flesh. Her nipples stood at attention like brand new Army recruits eager to please the drill sergeant. I licked my lips.

"Do you like what you see? Be honest," Lucky said, brushing away imaginary dirt on her perfectly round shoulder.

Speechless. I sat there. I didn't like what I saw. I loved it. But how did Lucky know that I was attracted to women? I never told her that.

"Shawn told me you guys had a threesome," she said, reading my mind. "Don't be mad at him."

"I'm not mad...just surprised. This explains why you're on camera looking like a whole ass meal," I said, flirting with her. Fuck it. The gloves were off.

Lucky squeezed her nipples and said my name with a voice so deep and melodical that I thought Anita Baker had entered the room. "Take off your clothes. I want to see you."

I obeyed. I did not realize I was touching myself until I heard her purr.

One hand caressed her breast while the other squeezed her yoni. "I wish these were your hands," she murmured.

The more I watched her, the wetter I became. Lucky kept saying my name as she rubbed her clit. With each touch her voice got deeper and deeper until she screamed my name and squirted. The jet stream almost hit the computer screen. Watching her took me over the edge as my own orgasm caused my body to erupt with pleasure. Exhausted, we sat there both of our chests quickly moving up and down as our heart rate returned to normal. Despite feeling a little bit guilty, I offered to come see her the following day.

"I can't wait," Lucky said, blowing kisses at me.

That night, I could barely sleep. Shawn picked up on it and asked why I was so restless. I sat up in bed and took an exaggerated breath before recounting the day's naughty, but nice, activities. His eyes flickered with anger and his hands folded into two tight fists.

"I cannot believe she did that!" Shawn yelled. He jumped out of bed and began walking around the room. He didn't bother to look at me.

Is this Negro really pacing? I thought. *Why is he in his feelings? Why is he so pissed?* "I thought you'd be turned on," I said, watching him stomp his bare feet across the carpet for the tenth time. "Is there something you are not telling me about you two?"

"I'm pissed," he said. He'd finally stopped moving and looked directly at me. He sounded like someone's father. "I told her you were off limits. Some things are forbidden. I feel like... she crossed the line."

I had no idea how much this would bother him. But if he felt so strongly about her not coming on to me, why would he tell her about my attraction to women? My gut told me there was more to this story. When he left to go to the restroom, I sent Lucky a quick text cancelling our plans. Nothing was worth the tension between me and Shawn. He returned and slid under the covers, leaving a noticeable space between us. But he curled up next to me when I told him that I'd killed my plans to see Lucky. Then, he drifted off to sleep.

I limited my interaction with Lucky, but I stayed active on Flames and avoided the chatrooms she normally frequented. I didn't want to tempt myself, or her. Things weren't quite the same. One Saturday night, while I was on the couch watching a movie and Shawn was on the computer playing a game, he popped up to head out into one of New York City's wannabe blizzards. The sky was dark and the clouds couldn't decide if they wanted to cover the city with twenty inches of snow.

"I'll be right back," he said, grabbing his coat and his phone. It rang a few times before he silenced it. Then he disappeared for fifteen minutes. When he unlocked the door, Lucky stood in the doorway with Shawn right behind him. He looked damn near giddy. My mind scrambled to make sense of the scene. Did they plan this?

"It feels good to be in the same room with you," Lucky said, walking over to wrap her arms around me for a long hug. She smelled like lilacs, soft and pretty, and she looked even better in person than on screen. Some women are naturally pretty without all the makeup and lashes and Lucky fell into that category. She was also one of those who could make a gray hoodie, matching Uggs and black leggings look like high fashion.

When I found my voice, I told her to make herself comfortable. Lucky peeled out of the hoodie and socks, to reveal a hot pink tank top and a fresh pedicure. Her bare feet tipped across the room and she sat next me on the couch. Clearly, Shawn had a change of heart about my special friendship with Lucky. We were all on chill mode for a while as I drank and Lucky and Shawn smoked a lil' weed. The conversation flowed. Shawn was ultra-relaxed and I could feel the chemistry between him and Lucky. He was enamored with her, practically hanging on to her every word. It didn't bother me at all because I was flattered that he'd arrange this for me.

"Put on some music! I feel like dancing," I told Shawn, as I leapt from the chair.

He turned on an R&B playlist. Once Bell Biv DeVoe started singing "Poison," I let loose with my old school dance moves.

"Go, Bree!" Lucky and Shawn cheered me on in unison until I collapsed on the couch. Shawn sat next to me and kissed me, deeply. Lucky sat on the opposite side of me and rubbed my thighs. When Shawn came up for air, she turned my face toward her to kiss me. Attention from both of them was intoxicating. Shawn stood in front of me, unzipped his pants and slowly stroked himself. Before he had his way with me, I told Lucky to take off her clothes. And I did the same.

Naked, I took her hand and led her to the shower. I got in first and she followed me. Lucky faced the wall as I lathered her up with my favorite cucumber melon scent shower gel. I washed her upper body and made my way down south. I made small, deliberate, but gentle circles on her ass. She gasped for air.

I grabbed the detachable shower head and rinsed the white soapy suds off her chocolate skin. She tried to turn around, but I wasn't finished. "Put your hands on the wall and spread your legs," I whispered in her ear. I dropped to a squat position, spread her second set of lips and stuck my tongue so deep in her that it caused me to moan.

"Don't stop," she begged, arching her back.

I had no intention of stopping. She arched her back even more, which gave me better access to her pretty pink clit. Her juices and the shower water ran down my face. I knew the neighbors heard her screaming my name.

Trembling legs and all, we made our way to the bedroom. Shawn waited patiently for us in the bed. We both took a side of the bed and left him in the middle as all three of us took turns sucking each other. After they both satisfied me, I fell into a light sleep.

When I woke up Shawn's head was buried between Lucky's legs. But I didn't say a word. I pretended to be asleep.

"Why are you doing me like this? I can't stop cummin'," she said. Her voice sounded like she was on the verge of tears.

"Do you know how long I wanted this? To taste you? To be inside you?" His voice was a low, soft growl. There was so much passion in his voice. Her legs were on his shoulders as he slid inside her with long, deep strokes. They were too engrossed in each other. Once he picked her up and fucked her against the wall, I slipped out of the house to a nearby park.

The New York hawk was out as a thin layer of snow lined the street.

My gut was right all along.

"He has feelings for her. The way he was fucking her, that's not just lust," I said aloud to myself. I sat on the park bench for thirty minutes, kicking myself for not asking more questions. I was angry at myself for falling into their trap and jealous of the way Shawn devoured her when he thought I wasn't looking. Tonight wasn't about the three of us, it was about him wanting to fuck her, for old time's sake.

When I got back to the house, Lucky, wearing her pink tank top and panties greeted me from the couch. I could hear the shower running and Shawn singing the chorus to "Poison" loud and off-key. "Beware she's schemin'. She'll make you think you're dreamin'. You'll fall in love and you'll be screamin' demon."

"Where did you go? I reached for you, but you weren't there." She smiled sheepishly.

"It didn't seem like I would be missed. I saw the way you two were going at it," I spat. My tone wreaked of venom. I'd never spoken to her like that before.

She tugged on her tank top's drooping spaghetti strap. "Maybe I should go…"

She must've let her voice trail off just in case there was a small part of me that wanted her to stay. I tossed her hoodie across the room and she stood up to catch it in mid-air. "Yeah, you should."

Lucky tried to plead her case, but I was in no mood for empty apologies. I locked the door behind her and poured myself another glass of wine and patiently waited for Shawn to exit the shower.

SESSION NO. 1: SUBMISSION

Can't seem to

catch my breath

It's running from me, my nectar is

slowly being sucked from me

Orgasms are arriving

In waves, I'm hopping

like the Energizer Bunny

He keeps whispering, "Baby, cum for me.

Yeah, just like that

I need more honey

Baby, ummm, you taste so yummy.

Climb off my face

and lay flat

on your tummy"

I do as I'm told

my body can't stop shaking

This man is out of control

He knows what he wants

so he takes it

Damn, he's sooooooo

erotic and bold

Lovemaking so elite

It's as if he's touching my soul

BODY FAX

Just got off the phone with you

On the 'Gram on your flicks, I just loved a few

Especially the ones when you got a fresh cut

and your is beard all groomed

Good jeans, nice sweater

Looking all brand new

You know my weakness

Nice teeth, clean sneakers

Crisp cologne on the collarbone

Whispering in my ear

In that sexy ass baritone

Telling me you can't wait 'til you get home

You just pulled up

There goes my ringtone, singing

Shawty, you 10

I pick up

You said, "Let me in."

I opened the door

Your tongue wants more

In my black lace nightie

I'm on all fours

I look up at you

You already know

what it is

I crawl away and you follow me in

Clothes are off and you're following me, face first

You're licking and lapping

Like your dying of thirst

Who am I not to allow

Your thirst to be quenched?

After that tongue you gave me

Every inch

I took every thrust

And I threw it right back

You know how I do

Check my body fax

It was everything I needed

And so much more

Round 2 will be in

The bed if we make it

Off the floor

SESSION NO. 3: THE HEAT

Glass of red wine
I'm sipping
the two of them
on the floor
touching and kissing
I can't help but notice
that my baby
is standing at attention
I'm totally engrossed
yes, they have
my full attention
this freak life
I thought I gave up
I was just in remission
Lust and this wine
got me slipping
got me crawling
across the floor
purring like a kitten
Now I'm laying
on my back
I'm sucking
while she's licking
In between slurps
I'm moaning,
"Don't stop

get it, get it"
 She saying
"Mami, you don't
have to worry
you taste fuckin' delicious"
I glazed her face
It's time to change positions
I told her
stand in front of
me so I can
tongue kiss it
as I arched my back
and prepared to go get it
Rounds and rounds
of deviant behavior
the taste of desire
on my lips, umm
I love the flavor
my body is feeling
beautifully beat
and terribly weak
It's great with 2
but there's so much
heat with 3

SESSION NO. 5: GOOD NIGHT

Lights are off just the

glare from the TV

Laying on the bed

hoping that he feeds me

Body is going through withdrawal

she needs to eat

Heat is coursing through me

I need release

Roll over to him

no real plan

Pull his cock out

Literally take matters

into my own hands

Tongue kiss the head

Slow lick the shaft

Caress his balls

Until he starts to gasp

Now I got him where

I want him

As I play with my clit

I begin to taunt him

in between moans

I talk my shit

Let him know that

I own his dick

in this moment there's a power shift

He pushes me down, my panties he rips

A moan escapes, I'm losing my breath

He puts my legs around his neck

Strokes me deep, the grind is so elite

Feels so good I start to weep

I'm speechless

He's playing for keeps

Feels like I'm dreaming

So, overwhelmed

I'm silently screaming

Words fail me

As he continuously tells me

"This yoni so good

You should be in jail, Cee."

Flood gates open

I'm shivering and shaking

I can't decipher

sounds that he's making

Fully satisfied, I close my eyes

Now that's how you tell

your lover goodnight

ELEVATOR

In close quarters, the air is thick

so close I can taste your lips

I can feel your hands on my hips

I close my eyes to control my breathing

I know this is wrong

But I don't plan on leaving

Part of me is very intrigued

When I open my eyes

You're on your knees

Against a wall I'm thrown

As your hands creep up my skirt

I begin to moan

Panties so wet as you push them aside

I position myself so you ease inside

As a warm rain builds between my legs

The strokes you inflict makes me beg

For you to please do bad things to me

That's when panties are ripped and fall

To my feet, you rise from the floor with

Such intensity turns me towards the wall

And slowly enter me. I'm grinding slow because

It feels so good to me

Your strokes are forceful

we have perfect chemistry

I can feel the orgasm on

the arrival and the way we

are mating, it almost feels primal

the moment we were waiting for is finally here

Words couldn't articulate the feeling

It was expressed through tears

As we fixed our clothes,

my eyes were shut

Who knew all this would happen?

Because the elevator got stuck

Normally, I take the stairs with pride

But I think I'm going to start

enjoying my elevator ride

KARAMEL DREAM (SIN SERIES)

When he walked in my
heart began to speed up
"Damn, baby," was what he
said as he watched me clean up
I bent over strategically so he could
see the heels that dressed my feet up
then I did a little stretch so he could admire
the wifebeater
I laughed to myself because
I knew I was wrong
I knew I drove him
crazy in the red lace thong
But I've been waiting on this all day long
Got on the tips of my toes and put my hands
Around his neck kissed him long and deep
'til he was erect
we parted lips
As he gazed at me he said,
"Damn, baby. Why are you playing with me?
Your sexy ass got on my favorite I see."
I smiled and sashayed away
I climbed on the counter
And spread my legs
"Come here," I whispered.
He just stared at me
I responded, "Baby, I know

you aren't scared of me."

He walked up to me took my breath away

started kissing from ankles slowed

down right before my waist

Looked down all I saw was desire on his face

tongue was so warm as it hit the lace

More moans escaped

"Baby, I love how your yoni tastes."

So much heat was on me, his tongue was doing laps

it was going so deep

he brought the sweetest pain on me

body on fire, I wish it would've rained on me

I love you, baby. You're my karamel dream

WET DREAM (SIN SERIES)

Walking slowly down a hall that's candle lit

different hands are pulling at me

As I search for an exit

some are from men bare chested

others are from women are exotically dressed

Music is in the air that's so inviting

As I approach a staircase

There appears to be two figures fighting

The closer I get I see I was mistaken

The moans are dead giveaway

of primal love making

I try to look away, but I'm so engrossed

I close my eyes and catch my breath

One of the figures comes close

As I open my eyes and exhale deeply

I see the most beautiful creature

Standing in front of me

Brown flesh, almond-shaped eyes, broad nose

Nice lips, firm thighs

flat stomach and nice round breast

She smiled at me and gestured with her finger

Looked me up and down as if

I was tonight's dinner

Grabbed my hand and led me to

the stairs where the other

Figure who was with her

Grabbed me by my hair

Pushed me down until

I was on all fours

Stood behind me

Whispered, "I want to enter your

back door."

Fear and excitement quickly engulfed me

He stroked my back

while she kissed me softly

Felt so good

I began a slow leak

Everything inside my mind

Screamed get off me, but the only words

That escape was, "Please don't stop."

My clothes began to get pulled off

With such ease, my yoni was on fire

Begging for release

Just as they were about

to devour me

Alarm clock went off

Fuck, another wet dream

WINTER'S STROLL (SIN SERIES)

We walk past a park

I start to smile

"Baby, can I have you?"

He damn near growls

His response was, "Baby, you know

you loud, when I beat it up

I might draw a crowd."

"Baby, stop playing,

I want you now."

Before I could blink

His pants were down

My skirt was up and my

legs were spread

felt so good when put in the head

When I want what I want

I don't need a bed

Body was hungry and was about to be fed

In and out, then came the circles

Had me so high like

I was puffing purple

Moaning so loud didn't care who was listening

First climax came, time to change positions

Started riding like I was in the derby

A church was nearby

I'm sure the parishioners heard me

I was grinding to the left

But he stayed in the middle

"Baby, if you stop. I swear I'll kill you."

He was so deep

I could barely breathe

Orgasm was so big

I was weak in the knees

He always knows exactly

what I need

As we proceeded to leave, we fixed our clothes

Still felt tingling in my toes

Felt a slight chill though

It wasn't cold

I love being spontaneous and bold

Spice is the variety of life

So, I've I been told

Who knew how much excitement could

Take place on a winter's stroll

HEAD GAMES (SIN SERIES)

He knows exactly what I like
Long strokes, deep kisses
make me beg 'til I cry
I can't deny, I was so excited
When I went to see him
I could barely hide it
The way he looks like he
was ready for riding
I closed my eyes and visualized him inside it
Walked in his crib, it was like a whirlwind
Grabbed my hair kissed me
until my head started to swim
Shit drove me crazy like he
lit a match to my skin
Dark skin, dark Caesar
teeth so bright, Polo shirt navy
Wife beater white, belt loosened
Jeans fell to floor
The length of the erection let
me know what the night had in store
Breathing is labored, endorphins are flowing
Only thing on my mind is him going in
Pushed me down to the bed
Pulled me down my pants
Panties pulled to the side
Tongue so deep it's

like he lived inside me

First orgasm sent me

into a frenzy of spasms

but I would not be out done

it was my turn to have him

I made him stand up

Because I like it in my face

His eyes rolled back when

I took my first taste

I made it disappear

I'm a fan of magic

And anything that wasn't

nailed down he tried to grab it

but he wasn't safe from my mission

and I would not stop until

he could not utter a sentence

When he finally reached his peak

He yelled, "You're relentless."

I smiled and swallowed

I always handle my business

THIS MUST STOP

This has got to stop
in the beginning, it was cool but now it's not
I hate looking over my shoulder and being deceitful
allowing my lust to drive me
after the first time, it became so easy
I would text you the time and location
and you would meet me
We'd began talking then the intense looks would start
kissing then caressing, slowly my legs would part
my heart would race,
breathing would become labored
Desire and heat were in your eyes
as perspiration fell from your face
Hands over my head
as you licked savagely
your tongue was so lethal
felt as if it was attacking me
legs around your neck
screaming for mercy
in between licks
you growled like you were thirsty
Tonight, I'm gonna
be your personal slurpy
over the edge, you pushed me
satisfied to the point
I didn't feel guilty

2 ROUNDS

We've been at it for a while
Damn, I want more
the last strokes were crazy
You activated my inner whore
Legs spread, 1 on the bed
1 on the floor
I'm 2 fingers deep
Umm, hitting my core
Orgasms are frequent
I really can't keep score
Sweating profusely
Like the air conditioner
ain't on
My body needs to be fed
Why is he not on?
I know he's turned on
He whispers, "Baby
Sometimes, I like
To watch you perform
I dare not interrupt
This scene is so strong
To intervene with
this masterpiece
Baby that would
just be wrong."
Next wave came

Lovesick

As I carried on

My body was pleased

Like it heard its favorite song

PART 3

STEAMY

TRADE IT ALL

"Have you ever thought about us being together?" I said, seductively, twisting one of my locs around my finger. My phone was in the perfect place cradled between my shoulder and my ear. "We've been doing this dance for quite some time."

"The way we started this thing, honestly, I can't see myself building anything with you," Jay said. His directness used to turn me on. Today, it knocked the wind out of me. He didn't soften the blow. He spoke to me as if I was a stranger, instead of his lover.

I stopped playing with my hair and hit the mute button. I let my tears roll freely, realizing that this was the end of our situationship. I met Jay a few months ago at Savor salon in Brooklyn. That day was the beginning of my downward spiral.

When I stepped inside Savor, I exchanged pleasantries with the regulars and my boy Sal. I couldn't help but notice the Cocoa Cutie seated in Sal's barber chair. Our eyes met and we both smiled fondly at each other. As I headed to the back of the salon to get my locs retwisted I overhead Sal say, "Oh, you like that," to his client.

Cocoa Cutie responded loud enough for me to hear, "Hell yeah. She got all the right weaponry."

I appreciated the rap reference from Mos Def's "Ms. Fat Booty," so I put a little extra bounce in my hips for his benefit, just to see if Sal's client could pick up what I was throwing down.

"Miss you gonna cause a traffic accident with the way you're moving that body," Cocoa Cutie informed me. The stylists and clients laughed at his joke.

"Keep your eyes on the road sir and you'll be fine," I said, playing it cool.

"My eyes are on the bumpa," he said in a faux Caribbean accent.

I liked his style. And it was easy for me to consider making time in my busy schedule for the guy who looked like he shared a bloodline with Idris Elba. My relationship had hit a speed bump and things were going downhill.

Chill, Taj, I thought to myself as I imagined sitting on Cocoa Cutie's face. *You got a man, so there's no need to be out here being a slut butt.*

I sat in my stylist's chair while she grabbed a few products and I pretended to be preoccupied with my phone. That was short lived.

Cocoa Cutie stood in front of me with a fresh line up and razor-sharp mustache and beard with the right amount of luster. I looked up and licked my lips to suck the drool back into my mouth.

"Definitely a Ricky Ross vibe," I mumbled as I secretly admired Sal and God's handiwork.

To me and my girls, if men gave great bread, they went in the Rick Ross category. God blessed this chocolate dream with height (my calculations read six feet, two inches), broad shoulders, big brown eyes and full lips. He had the kind of lips that could cool a bowl of chicken noodle soup with one strategic blow.

"Stop staring at me. You're making me nervous," I said, teasing him.

He smirked and leaned in close to whisper in my ear. "Make me stop." His voice sounded like an interlude on a '90s R&B album.

I wasn't prepared for his response, so I took a deep breath and waited for something cute and clever to tumble out of my mouth. But it didn't happen. Cocoa Cutie knocked me off my game for a minute. I shifted my weight in my seat. He enjoyed watching me squirm. A hush hung in the air as he held my gaze and then walked toward the restroom near the back of Savor.

When the door closed, I scurried over to ask Sal about his fine-ass customer. Sal told me he was happy to hook me up with Jay, but I didn't need a matchmaker. I just wanted a character résumé, when I didn't get one, I hurried back to my seat. Cocoa Cutie, better known as Jay, returned and stuffed a few crisp bills in Sal's hand. They dapped each other up and Sal, with his eyes locked on me, lowered his voice as he spoke to Jay.

I shot Sal the death stare. He shrugged his shoulders and summoned the next client.

Just then, a seat opened up next me as another stylist guided her client to the dryer. Jay took the woman's place beside me and dragged his pointer finger down my thigh. His touch was electric.

"So, Taj. I hear that you've been asking about me. I'd like to get your number. I can tell you all there is to know."

Drunk off his YSL cologne, which is my favorite, I barely heard what Jay said. But I couldn't let him get the best of me again.

"I like a man that's direct, so I'm sure you appreciate a woman who can do the same. I have a man," I said flatly, returning to pressing random apps on my phone.

Jay wasn't the least bit fazed. "I have a girl, but I won't lie, I'm interested." He took my phone and punched his number on the keypad and saved his contact information. "Take my number instead."

Three days later, I sent Jay a text with a sexy picture to jog his memory about meeting me at Savor. Immediately, my phone lit up with his response. "I thought you forgot about me. I was about to give up hope."

Jay was hard to forget, but I wasn't about to let him know that.

"I've been busy," I lied via text.

"Well, I'm glad you made time in your schedule," he replied, including the smiley face emoji.

We made plans to speak the next day. After our initial call, we spoke daily for three weeks. His attention and compliments were water for my self-esteem drought, especially since I wasn't getting them at home.

When we decided to meet for drinks, I changed clothes three times before slipping into a green fitted dress and gold sandals. My outfit was chic and sexy without trying too hard. I spritzed perfume on my neck and wrists and swiped a mocha gloss on my lips.

We met at a Brazilian restaurant in Park Slope. The decor was nice, but it was no match for Jay.

He made a simple white T-shirt and black jeans seem like a couture fit. The diamond stud in his ear competed with the brightness of his smile. Jay's eyes soaked me and made me feel like there was no other woman in the place. I bit my bottom lip to calm the butterflies in my stomach. He scooped me into his massive chest for a hug and it felt good to be in his protective arms.

The waiter sat us at a table for two near the window. Like a gentleman, Jay pulled out my seat.

"I was so nervous about tonight," I said, glancing at the menu.

"We're both doing something we've never done before. Let's just enjoy the evening. No pressure, okay?" Jay said, sliding his hand across the table to touch mine. They were soft, like he spent a grip on expensive hand cream. We relaxed in our seats and ordered drinks.

We left the spot around ten o'clock and neither of us was ready to go home. He suggested we go for a drive and we ended up at Brooklyn Bridge Park. We walked for a bit before relaxing on a bench. Jay pulled me in close as we stared at the Manhattan lights across the Hudson River. "Are you enjoying yourself?"

"Yes," I answered, sounding more breathless than I'd intended. I snuggled my face deep into his chest to inhale his scent, then I came up to chase it with night air. His eyes locked with mine. It's been a minute since I've had this much fun."

"Good," Jay said, placing a finger underneath my chin. He lifted my face to meet his and slipped his tongue inside my mouth. I returned the favor with an eagerness that surprised us both.

Things were getting steamy so we stopped and walked it off. We ended up by a railing overlooking the river. Jay kissed me again and pressed his erection into my sundress.

The feeling was more than mutual, and at first, I played like an innocent angel, knowing that my intentions were straight devilish. I took his hand and guided it down my dress over my nipples, until he reached my mid-section. I spread my legs and lifted the front of my dress to the side, along with my lace panties. My yoni pulsated in his hands as he rubbed my clit. His facial expressions had me in my zone. I had him right where I wanted him, or so I thought, until he squeezed my yoni. I thought I was going to explode. I unbuckled his jeans just enough to reach my hand inside so I could stroke his engorged masterpiece.

Jay clenched his teeth, "Let's go. Because if we don't, I'm gonna fuck you right here and I don't care who sees us."

I liked the idea of him fucking me outside and the possibility of us getting caught, but we fixed our clothes and headed to the car. I got in the front seat and reclined so I could get comfortable, while he fiddled around in the trunk. Ready to explode, I took my panties off and started touching myself. I stuck my middle finger inside of my wet middle while my thumb made circular motions on my clit. I rode the wave that Jay started and it felt so good. Jay watched me from the outside of the car. I love an audience so I didn't stop my performance until I dripped all over his seat. I never took my eyes off him as I sucked my juices off my fingers. Once I was done, I smoothed my dress into place and stuffed my panties into my bag.

"You're definitely going to have me open," Jay said, getting into the backseat of the car. He handed me a condom." That was some sexy shit, Taj."

I grinned and took the wrapper from his hand. It was empty. "What am I supposed to do with this?" I said.

He unzipped his pants to show me what he did with the condom. "Jump on this dick right now."

I obliged, climbing on top and lowering myself onto his massive pole. Slowly, I bounced my hips up and down and he matched my speed. We continued that way for a few minutes each movement became more intense. He spread my ass and gripped my cheeks for dear life as he convulsed in short sporadic movements. I moaned with pleasure.

"Fuck! What are you trying to do to me?" he said, pumping a few more times.

I laid on his chest as we both sat there sweaty and breathing hard.

He broke the silence. "So when can I see you again?"

"Soon," I said, mentally clearing things off my calendar for our next link up. "Very soon."

Spending time with Jay led me to daydream about him being my man. I was so caught up that I started comparing Rob to Jay, something I said that I'd never do. But Jay always had time for me and he made me feel beautiful and desired. Plus, whenever we hung out people automatically assumed I was Jay's lady. Then, something changed. When Jay's relationship ended, I thought this meant I'd see more of him. Our weekly lunches stopped and then he'd ghosted me for two weeks.

I never complained because I knew what it was. He wasn't mine and I had to play my position. I figured he'd met someone else and my suspicions were confirmed when I saw another woman in his car. I saw him drop her off three blocks away from Savor. That night he called me and got right to the point. "Taj, you said if I want more from you I should be upfront, right?"

I braced myself, thinking this was the moment that would change everything. "Have you ever thought about us being together?" I said, seductively, twisting one of my locs around my finger. My phone was in the perfect place cradled between my shoulder and my ear. "We've been doing this dance for quite some time."

"The way we started this thing, honestly, I can't see myself building anything with you," Jay said. He didn't soften the blow. He spoke to me I was a stranger, instead of his lover. His directness used to turn me on. Today, it knocked the wind out of me. I stopped playing with my hair and hit the mute button. I let my tears roll freely, realizing that this was the end of our situationship.

"Hey, you there?" he said. His voice was a bit warmer than before.

"Yeah, I'm here,"

"Look, I'm just being honest. You know I care about you, but I need someone who is faithful."

What the fuck? I couldn't believe this fool was requiring loyalty as if he wasn't guilty of the same shit. "Are you done?" I said, cutting him off in the middle of his holier than thou speech. "Thanks for letting me know." I hung up without saying goodbye.

"What the fuck were you thinking, Taj?" I yelled at myself. "You were about to risk it all for this? For a man who couldn't see himself in a serious relationship with you?"

My phone buzzed. It was Jay. I declined the call and then removed his number from my contacts. Jay never promised me anything, while Rob offered me his heart and a future. I allowed myself to get caught up in the stolen moments, the sex, the secret lunches, the gifts and the what ifs. I gambled everything on someone who didn't deserve me. Would Rob ever forgive me?

GUD MOANING

Clothes coming off at a rapid pace

Heart beating at an unmeasurable rate

Moans escaped as our hands explored

The sensations I was feeling had me floored

I moaned in the air as he whispered in my ear

"Baby, do you mind if I put it right here."

I arched my back as he approached my rear

It felt so good as he pumped vigorously

While pulling my hair

I hardly recognized my own voice

As I screamed and whimpered 'til

I was damn near hoarse

Bites to my neck, several smacks to my ass

Caressed my breast as he pleasured my cat

A happy ending was approaching

I came so hard I didn't know if

I was coming or going

"Damn, that was good,"

he said with a laugh

I rocked myself to sleep

While he rubbed my back

Smiling to myself

I know he loved that

JUST US

All alone in my zone
Thoughts of lovemaking
Can't wait for
you to get home
Dinner's done
Body's bathed
House is clean
Hopefully you're
on your way
So much
to tell you
While we lay
As we sip chilled
Lemonade mixed
with Bombay
You the bomb Bae
I'll wash your back
while you tell me
about your day
Smiling damn near giddy
It's taking great restraint
not to stroke this kitty
Baby you're the only 1
that has the ability
to soak this kitty
After that

Lovesick

I need you to
to fuck this pussy
Summer dress
No panties on
you can't resist me

ANOTHER DAY AT THE OFFICE

I'm home
alone finally
A chance to
gather my thoughts
and just breathe
I saw him today
I tried to
avoid him today
When we were
together he never
had this
much to say
I was sitting
at my desk
he kept
eyeing me
Whenever I walk
by he brushes
against me seductively
he kept trying me
Eventually I found
some solace near
the file cabinet
next to the
coat closet
Took a few

Lovesick

minutes to collect
myself, butterflies in
my stomach
Under my blouse
yes, there was a swell
Between my
legs there
was a puddle
beginning to well
In front of
him I'm calm,
cool and collected
But in the
back of my
mind I want to
see him naked
Thank God my
poker face is
legit and he'd
never detect it
Took a deep
breath and headed
back to my desk
That's when I
felt a tug
to my wrist
turned around

and pulled me

right into his

arms and aggressively

licked my lips

then planted a

kiss, I tried to

resist but he

was hell bent

the more I

pulled away the

harder he went

The longer we

kissed the

further he went

His hands

were everywhere

unnerving me

was his intent

Just when I

thought he was

about to go

in he got page

over the P.A. system again

SELF-INFLICTED

Parental discretion is advised,

this is explicit

He is skilled,

dare I say gifted

He can get it

Can't wait for

him to get it

But until he does

self-inflicted

self-indulgence

that's what I'll do

in his absence

Give myself multiples

I'm under this AC

Wishing he was under me

up in me

Creating a wedge between

these knees, smacking and biting

on my cheeks

pounding so deep

Stroking me into submission

without any breaks, just sweet release

The asthma pump is nearby

'cause it's hard to breathe

POWER OF THREE

They don't know
what my life be 'bout
Wife type shit, yet
I'm rubbing one out
Hubby in the next
room making her shout
When you're into multiples
someone is bound
to feel left out
Playing in these worlds
can make the strongest
person have doubts
This right here ain't for
the faint at heart
you better know this is
what you want
before you start
I guess flirting for me is enough
I always renege whenever
someone wants to link up
I like threesomes
I can admit to that
I don't like that one on one
They can keep that,
see I know how my man beats it up
Have a chick climbing the

Lovesick

wall while he's eating it up

Conversation all spicy,

he is heating things up

My biggest fear is someone falling in love

all I can do is be honest and trust

that these lusts filled nights

never come between us

LOVE ON MY MIND

I got love on my mind

While his head is between my thighs

Tongue kissing my kitty

I'm about to cry

I don't recognize my own voice

"Why does it feel like this?"

"Why does it feel so good?"

He growls

"You know how I do.

You knew it would.

Now, be still

Let me devour that clit

And when I'm done

you're gonna handle this dick."

I'm so submissive

He's so relentless

Orgasms on repeat

I'm so defenseless

I got love on my mind

While his head is between my thighs

I've got tears in my eyes

Making love to the love of my life

PLEASE ME

Thoroughly pleased
Heartbeat regulated
You were on your bully
Damn you regulated
Body throbbing with pleasure
Is an understatement
To say you were phenomenal
Isn't overstating
Was it the
Strength in your hands
You used to restrain me
Or the pleasurable reprimands
That they gave me
Your hands were
in the demand
As you gave me
verbal commands
You tied mine over my head
With a satin band
Chocolate syrup drizzled
Over my body
Sensory overload
Kissing on my thighs
I was losing control
Thoroughly pleased
Shivering at the thought
Of the memory

SELF-PLEASING

Legs spread wide open in a dark room
heavy breathing
body's wide awake
my honey is sleeping
touching myself quietly
hoping he ain't peeking
on the brink of the big O
umm, I'm tweaking
circular motions
in the middle of my yoni
came through dripping, literally
can't stop moaning
sounds like a symphony
now I wish he was awake
so he could finish me
gripping my waist
shots to the face
would replenish me
but I'mma let him rest
tomorrow, I'll take all of his energy

CANDY RAIN

Against the wall, hands above my head

You are licking profusely

Feels like I'm

gonna fall

Trembling from my toes to my thighs

I'm singing your name and whining my hips

You're spreading my cheek

Gently licking my lips

While tongue kissing my clit

4 orgasms in

About to be on my 5th

"Oh shit... right there

Please don't stop."

You oblige my request

I'm so wet

And your tongue

is my mop

I'm making crazy faces while screaming

your name

Damn, you always make my candy rain

THE CLIMAX

For as long as I can remember, whenever life tossed me a curveball or there was drama at home or in my neighborhood, writing was my safe space and reading was my escape. Reading was magical to me and it inspired me to write stories and poems and now this book.

Lovesick is my baby. But this project almost didn't happen. I made excuses about why I didn't have the time to write a book because I was busy performing spoken word and hosting poetry events. I got a rush from performing, especially my erotic pieces, in front of a live audience. Then, I got this nagging feeling (in a good way) that I should share my poetry and stories on a larger platform. But then I tried to talk myself out of it. I told myself that it would cost too much, that poetry is a hard sell and I worried about being successful. Deep down, I worried about how people would respond to my erotic fiction, especially since these stories feature messy threesomes and infidelity. I feared that my wild imagination would be judged by friends and family. Our society is obsessed with sex, but some people still see threesomes as taboo, but somehow it's fine for movies or porn.

I've talked to friends, men and women, who've given me their honest take on thrilling and messy threesomes. The triple play isn't for everybody. So if you're considering having a threesome, implement some ground rules. Both of you should feel comfortable, not just him. There is also the other party, she can catch feelings too. There are some cases where the other party becomes so attached that she actually thinks she can replace you. This world is not something you can enter in without careful consideration. And I cannot stress how important it is to use protection for everyone's safety. There's no need to kill the fun with an STD as a party favor.

Before you slip into something more comfortable, here are a few questions to ask yourself:

1) Am I jealous?

2) Am I attracted to women?

3) Do I trust my partner?

There are pros and cons to this adventure and there's so much to consider, but these three questions are a great starting point. If you're the type to flip if your partner respectfully admires another woman's beauty and curves, then tell Pandora to close her box of goodies and back away from the forbidden fruit. If you aren't attracted to women and the idea of receiving (or giving) head from a woman doesn't cause your kitty to ache with delight, then this game is not for you. And third, if you cannot trust your partner not to catch feelings for the other person or sneak around with this woman behind your back, then play it safe and go back to watching romantic comedies on the couch with Bae.

If you're still curious about having a threesome, think long and hard about it by yourself before talking about it openly and honestly with your partner.

BONUS HEAT

YOU GOT ME

YOU GOT ME

NNEKA

They say if you go looking for something, you'll find it, especially in a man's phone. I learned that lesson the hard way. Five days. That's how long it took before I caved and decided to search the contents of Jason's burner cell phone. The one he claimed was just for "games, music and bullshit." But he was always a little too protective of that device and something told me he was hiding more than just a playlist on here. Like most men, he was a horrible liar. So I pretended not to notice when he slipped the old phone into a box of Jordans.

"Just do it, Nneka," I said to myself as I opened his walk-in closet.

"Seek and you will find." My mother's words were on repeat in my head as I ran my fingers along his perfectly aligned collection of kicks, trying to remember which box housed the phone. "Not this one. Not this one," I said, carefully moving his prize possessions until I hit the jackpot. I sat on the bed and took a deep breath. Now that it was in my hands, I couldn't resist a slow scroll into Jason's business. It was Friday and Jason was probably with his boy Speedy downing his second Jack and Ginger at KoKo Moe's bar. He was a creature of habit and very predictable.

"Fuck it," I said, tapping the screen. The smartphone sprang to life, but it was password protected. It took three attempts to guess the code: 10 24 56. Bingo, his mama's birthday. Being a liar and being predictable wasn't a winning combo for him.

There were multiple shots of his situation and videos of him stroking it until he released his creamy insides on the sheets. I made a mental note to check the deleted photos folder for more hidden gems, after I watched all of his little home movies. My heart stopped when I saw the woman's face in the latest video. It was my girl Ashley. Quickly, I scrolled to see if she was featured in any others and she was. The oldest clip was five years ago, after Speedy's annual '90s house party. I shook my head from left to right as if my eyes were deceiving me, but they weren't. Ash walked toward the bed in a Morehouse T-shirt that I'd purchased for Jason.

"You like what you see?" Ashley asked the person off camera. She placed the tip of her middle finger in her mouth and sucked it, slowly.

It turned out Jason wasn't lying. There was some "bullshit" on this phone. I shook my head as if my eyes were deceiving me, but they weren't. I knew about that one-time sexcapade that happened when they both got a little tipsy at Speedy's party. I spent that weekend preparing slides for a big vegan baby food marketing presentation, so I skipped the bash. Jason swore their hook up was a mistake. That it meant nothing. "It only lasted about five minutes, maybe four," he said. Maybe he meant to say four or five times after the house party, because these photos told a different story. But at the time Jason sounded sincere. He was convincing. I'll give him that.

And although I was hurt, I blamed myself for neglecting him (I was so busy chasing a marketing promotion) that I forgave him...and Ashley. She begged me with tears and a snotty nose not to whip her ass and to preserve a friendship that dated back to middle school. We kinda patched things up but I was distant. And she definitely wasn't welcome to be a third when I hung out with Jason. Ash lost those privileges the minute she fucked my man for four or five minutes, or four or five times, or four or five years.

The entire video gallery seemed like a TV series entitled *Ashley's Freakiest Home Videos*. There were at least seven recent clips of Ash playing with herself in a hotel bedroom, including one from yesterday afternoon when he was supposed to be at work. In the video, she spread her legs wide and rubbed her swollen clit for six minutes and fifty-three seconds.

It was some *Guinness Book of World Records* shit and I couldn't stop watching. Not because I was aroused, but because of Jason's voice. He sounded different. Warm and sexy. There was a longing in his voice that he used to have for me. He complimented Ash's body and told her that she was beautiful, words he'd never said to me the whole time we were together. Instead, he chose to remind me that he didn't date curvy women. Jason preferred "the slim goodies." I should've told him that I preferred eight inches, but that would've been a petty comeback. True, but petty.

The videos showed more than just a physical connection. It looked like they cared for each other. There were clips of them discussing her non-profit for teen girls, church and the latest Jordan Peele movie. Imagining the phone was Jason's neck, I gripped it tight and fought back tears as a small fire burned in the pit of my stomach. My insides grew hot and I had the urge to throw something and break it into a thousand pieces. I snatched the vase filled with purple and yellow asters off the dresser and hurled it at the yellow accent wall. The bouquet was yesterday's gift with a note declaring his "devotion" to me. More lies. More bullshit. What did MC Lyte say? "Guys be running games like the New York Knicks."

"Why, Jay? Why? Why am I not enough?" I wailed into the empty room.

I grabbed things, watches, bottles of cologne, sunglasses and flung them across the room. My body spun around and around like a tornado and picked up speed until I dropped to the floor. My chest heaved up and down as I surveyed the beautiful mess in Jason's room. Once I regained my balance, I tiptoed across the parquet floor careful not to cut my bare feet. I jammed the phone into the back pocket of my jeans and grabbed my sandals and headed toward the door. But I caught a glimpse of myself in Jason's full-length mirror. My curls were wildly out of place with a stray piece of flower stuck in my strands and my so-called waterproof mascara didn't do its job. My gray wife beater was twisted. "Pull it together, Nneka," I said, grabbing some makeup wipes from my bag. "You can do this."

As I swept the black mascara from underneath my eyes, my mother's words played on loop in my head: "Nneka you are beautiful. You are worthy and most of all you are loved. Jay doesn't deserve you. It's time for you to realize that. You don't need to break into his apartment."

"I'm looking for that phone, Ma. I have to see what he's hiding," I'd told her earlier that day. My voice sounded pathetic and weak.

"Seek and you will find," she cautioned.

"I know, Ma."

"Yeah, but what are you going to do when you find it? Are you going to finally break up with him, Nneka?"

"I think so."

"Think?" My mother sounded irritated, again. She'd been down this road with me after his whole tipsy sex fiasco with Ash. "You stole his key while he was asleep, made a copy and you *think* you're going to break up with him. You think? Girl, do you hear yourself?"

"Ma, please. I love him."

She sighed. "Nneka, baby I don't think you know what love is."

Replaying that conversation with my mother snapped me back to my senses. She was right. It was time for me to stop allowing Jason to lie to me, to make a fool of me. I pulled my hair into a messy puff on top of my head and applied two coats of brick red lipstick. A red lip always made me look pulled together, even in a T-shirt and jeans. I locked the door with the secret key and headed to KoKo Moe's to confront Jason. But about a block away from the bar, I stopped short and sent him a text: "Game over." Then I turned around and headed toward the subway. Before I hit the bottom step Jason called. I sent him straight to voicemail.

JASON

All I want to do is chill with Speedy and smoke a little something when I get home. But Speedy finally got the green light from some girl he's been texting for three months, so he's downing the last swallow of Henny before heading to the Bronx.

"I'm out," Speedy said, giving me a pound.

"Yo, I hope shortie is worth the gas money, and the wait," I said, finishing the last buffalo wing.

"It's a gamble, but she just sent me a pic," he said, staring at his phone. "And the way she twisted herself into a pretzel to get this money shot? She knows what's up."

"It couldn't be me, bro. I'm not waiting three months to smash. She's on that Steve Harvey make-him-pass-the-probation-period-bullshit," I said, laughing.

Speedy counted thirty dollars for his share of the drinks and wings and slid it under his empty glass. "Shit, I'd rather wait six months than do the grimy shit you're doing."

That comment would've offended a regular ass nigga. I grabbed Speedy's money and waved the waitress over to catch the bill. "You know how I do. I'm not turning down pussy if it's right there in my face. Ashley knows how to play her position. She's cool with it."

"Yeah, that's what every man thinks before the side piece catches feelings and shit explodes." He slapped my back and headed out the door. "Catch you later."

This shit with Ashley is kinda out of control, but I got a handle on it. I don't like to compare Nneka and Ash, but Ash got that griminess that I can definitely relate to, but she wouldn't do me dirty. Plus, she makes these videos that drive me crazy. My sex life with Nneka is bomb, but I'm not as attracted to her as I used to be. She kinda let herself go with that extra weight she gained. I love her but I like doing me. I know it's some selfish shit, but it's true.

I scribbled a generous tip for the waitress and then noticed the text on my phone. It read: "Game over." It was from Nneka. She could be cryptic at times with her messages, so I called her twice, but it went to voicemail. I sent her a text: "Heading home. Call me."

The engine purred as I thought about calling Ashley and as if on cue a text from T.B. Head popped up. That's Ash's code name. It's short for The Best Head. She's playing pool in lower Manhattan.

"Pull up. Lemme buy you a drink… and give you something special in the bathroom," she wrote with a wink emoji.

Ash had this sixth sense to know either when me and Nneka were fighting or when she was ignoring my calls. Tonight Nneka was sending my shit to voicemail. My dick started to rise just thinking about sneaking off to meet Ash in the bathroom. I dropped a quick text before wheeling into traffic. "Be there in twenty minutes."

ASHLEY

He's such a good boy, I thought to myself after reading Jason's text. *He doesn't just jump when I give a command. He asks, "How high?"*

The bartender handed me my New York Sour and took my card. "Can I start a tab for you, miss?" he asked. I took a sip and nodded. I would need another drink before Jason arrived. I'd let him win the first two games of pool, then wipe the floor with him. Being defeated turned him on and losing would inspire him to blow my back out like he has shit to prove.

I'm kinda happy that me and Nneka are still cool after she found out about me and Jason. At first, she lost it, threatened to beat my ass and all that, but then she caught herself. 'Cause she's such a fuckin' lady. Yeah, right. She told me that fighting another Black woman was beneath her.

The truth is she probably thought Jason's behavior was karma for focusing on work instead of her man or maybe she had her own indiscretions. I've seen the way those suit and tie niggas be all up on her. She had to get down with at least one of them.

Ugh, but I hate how open minded she thinks she is. Open minded. Oh, that's what we're calling it now? It's more like foolish to me. If the shoe was on the other foot, we would have definitely been fighting like a *Love & Hip-Hop* reunion show because I want Jason. All of him. Not just these bits and pieces he gives me in between his daily life with Nneka. But I'll just play my position until the time is right. I might accidentally send her a video of me and him or just one of me, naked on her bed. That might get her attention.

In the meantime, I'll ride Jason's face whenever I like. Shoot, it's not like her fat ass can. What does he see in her? If she got her shit together maybe he wouldn't be all over me, fucking the life out of me on the sheets she bought. And if she wants to keep him, Nneka should quit nagging him and ignoring his calls. It just makes it easier for me.

Jason told Nneka our link up was just "five minutes of pleasure" and that it didn't mean anything. And she believed that shit? I thought my girl was smarter than that. It's more like five years of pleasure. And I'm about to play homeless, so that I can live in Jason's spare bedroom. Nneka thought I was done, huh? Bitch, I'm just getting started.

To be continued...

ACKNOWLEDGMENTS

Some journeys are meant to be traveled alone, but a team of folks had my back on this one. And for that, I'm truly grateful. Your support and encouragement has overwhelmed me in the best way. My list of people to thank is endless, so I'll try to keep it short and sweet.

Latayia Hicks, thank you bestie for always having my back and encouraging me to push through, especially when I didn't think I could. I love you and appreciate your support.

Niecy Rivera, my bestie from college! Girl, you loved me despite my inability to type. You encouraged me to write a book (starting with a greeting card line) and look, my dream is now my reality. You believed in me and you saw the vision—before I did. I love you for that and so much more.

My soul sisters: Adrienne and Stephanie. Adrienne, you never let me forget that I made a promise to myself to write a book in 2020 and you were determined to make sure that I stuck to my plan. Stephanie, thank you for being the ultimate prayer warrior. You'd pray for me and with me and offer an encouraging word, but more importantly, you gave me a non-judgmental ear. I love you for that.

Leonna, my poetic, lyrical friend. I love you, sis. You're one of the reasons I decided to perform my poetry onstage. You praised my writing and encouraged me to show off my talent. Your advice, as a published author, has been invaluable on this journey. Thank you for being one of my biggest cheerleaders.

I have the best family in the world and that's no exaggeration, right down to my aunties, uncles, cousins, nieces and nephews. Pamela, Joseph, Tyro, Shauda, Tyrone, my sisters and brothers, thank you for being my ride-or-die crew. Family is important to me and your support is unmatched.

Last, but never least, my big sis and the best editor ever, Taiia Smart Young. You've helped me become a better writer. You made this journey fun and I learned a lot. I cannot wait to write the next book.

And to anyone who's read any of my work, I'm beyond thankful to you.

ABOUT THE AUTHOR

Kareema Edwards was born in Brooklyn, New York in the winter of 1975. She's been married to the love of her life Teddy Edwards for nineteen years. Kareema is the mother of Kareem and Seona and grandmother of Isaiah a.k.a. Pumpkin Butt. When Kareema's in chill mode she enjoys reading, writing, performing at open mics and spending time with family and friends. Kareema has also been published in *Voices From The Sisterhood, Spiritual Reflections*, Vol. 1, and her poem "It's Not a Waste of Time" was featured in a Telly Award winning commercial for the Department of Sanitation.

Thank you for reading

Lovesick: Poems & Stories to Turn You On

If you touched yourself, bit your bottom lip or sent a naughty text to Bae while reading this book, use those sticky fingers to type an online review at Amazon.com.

Seriously, even if you didn't do any of the above, reviews are everything to new (and established) authors, so hook me up, okay? I promise that it will make you feel good.

Let's connect on Instagram: @YellowTale_1

Made in the USA
Columbia, SC
07 March 2021

34005098R00071